Super Special Magic Shoes

ISBN 978-1-7375936-1-4

Printed in the USA

This book is dedicated to
my beautiful Isabella.

May you have many joyful adventures
with your Super Special Magic Shoes!

Super Special Magic Shoes

Written by
Megan Marie Higgins

Illustrated by
Daria Shamolina

My muscles work differently than other friends of mine.

My legs need a little help
to walk, run, jump and climb.

Some kids wear glasses
to help them see far or near.

Others might need hearing aids, special devices for your ears.

I wear Super Special Magic Shoes that give each foot a hug.

They help me stand tall and proud
or dance the jitterbug.

**Super Special Magic Shoes
come in different lengths.**

Each one helps develop our
super special strengths.

Some go to your hips.

Some go to your knees.

Mine go to my ankles,

made special just for me.

I get to choose the color I want:
red, yellow, green, blue...

any color from the rainbow -
pick your favorite hue!

Select a favorite pattern.
There are so many to choose.

I love hearts or stars or butterflies,
even flying spaceships too!

All my friends like my shoes.
They think they're pretty cool.

I can't wait to show them off
to everyone at school.

I work hard to build my muscles
every single day.

My most important job is to
move around and play.

Every time I wear my shoes
my legs shout, "HOORAY!"

I am excited to begin another
happy, fun-filled day.

Super Special Magic Shoes help me
walk, run, jump and more.

Together, we have fun adventures.
There is a whole world to explore!

Super special magic shoes are leg braces for super, special kids. They help your legs and muscles by improving balance, tone and strength

Types of leg braces

SMO: Supramalleolar Orthosis is a brace that covers your foot and ankle.

AFO: Ankle Foot Orthosis is a brace that goes to just below the knee.

KAFO: Knee Ankle Foot Orthosis is a brace that extends the whole leg.

HKAFO: Hip Knee Ankle Foot Orthosis is a brace that extends the whole leg with a pelvic band attached.

How Super Special Magic Shoes Are Made

An Orthotist, a health care provider who specializes in making and fitting medical supportive devices, make and fit children for their braces. Some measure your foot and some use the cast method.

How Isabella's SMOs Are Made

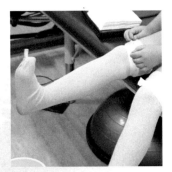

Step 1: Put on special socks.

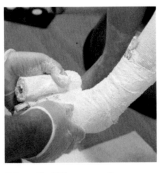

Step 2: Wrap wet plaster around foot and leg.

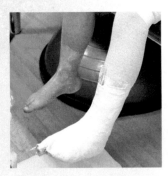

Step 3: Wait for it to dry and harden.

Step 4: Snip off the dry form.

Step 5: Give the form to your Orthotist.

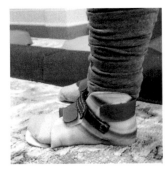

Step 6: Wear your Super Special Magic Shoes!

Author
Megan Marie Higgins

Megan Marie Higgins first began her storytelling adventure after her adorable daughter started wearing super special magic shoes. She was never able to find a book that described how wonderful these shoes are to wear. Inspired by her daughter, Isabella, she wanted to create a fun, joyful story about these cool shoes and represent leg braces in a positive way. Megan enjoys bringing awareness to special needs issues in a fun and happy light. She loves children's literature and how it can spark imagination and creativity.

Megan resides in Akron, OH with her husband and their beautiful daughter. They enjoy fun adventures and traveling the world. Megan loves being a mommy and playing, snuggling and reading with her daughter. Her favorite activities are baking, holiday decorating, anything Disney and, most importantly, spending time with her friends and family.

Illustrator
Daria Shamolina

Daria began her illustrating adventure at the age of 14 when she was hired for her first job at a newspaper created by teenagers. She later studied at her local University and began professionally publishing soon after. Daria has illustrated multiple children's books and has a special talent for creating adorable, colorful and bright characters.

Daria resides in the Ukraine with her son, Daniel. He is the greatest love of her life! Becoming a mommy has made all her dreams come true. Daria's favorite activity is going to the zoo with her son and enjoying the many different types of animals together.